First published 2007 by Boxtree
an imprint of Pan Macmillan, a division of Macmillan Publishers Limited
Pan Macmillan, 20 New Wharf Road, London N1 9RR
Basingstoke and Oxford
Associated companies throughout the world
www.panmacmillan.com

ISBN 978-0-7522-2660-6

Text and illustrations copyright (c) Modern Toss Limited, 2007
PO Box 386, Brighton BN1 3SN, England
www.moderntoss.com

The right of Jon Link and Mick Bunnage to be identified as the
authors of this work has been asserted by them in accordance
with the Copyright, Designs and Patents Act 1988.

9 8 7

A CIP catalogue record for this book is available from the British Library

Designed and typeset by Modern Toss Limited
Printed and bound in China

Visit www.pan ... about all our books and to buy them. You will also find features,
author i ... o that

THE MODERN TOSS GUIDE TO

Work

by Jon Link and Mick Bunnage

B⬡XTREE

successful applicant

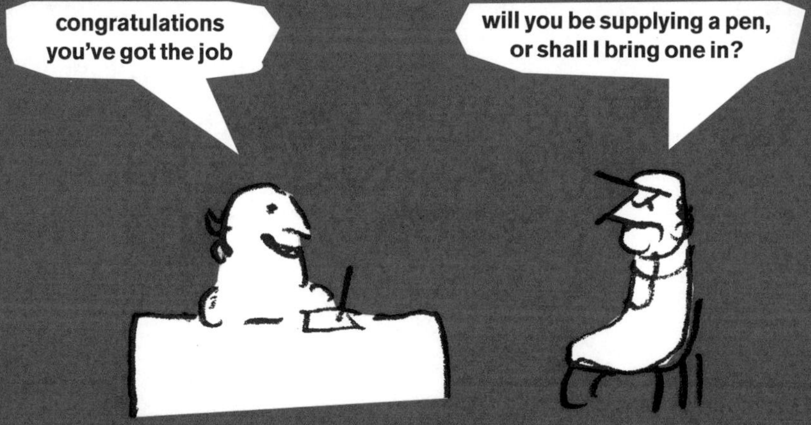

interview

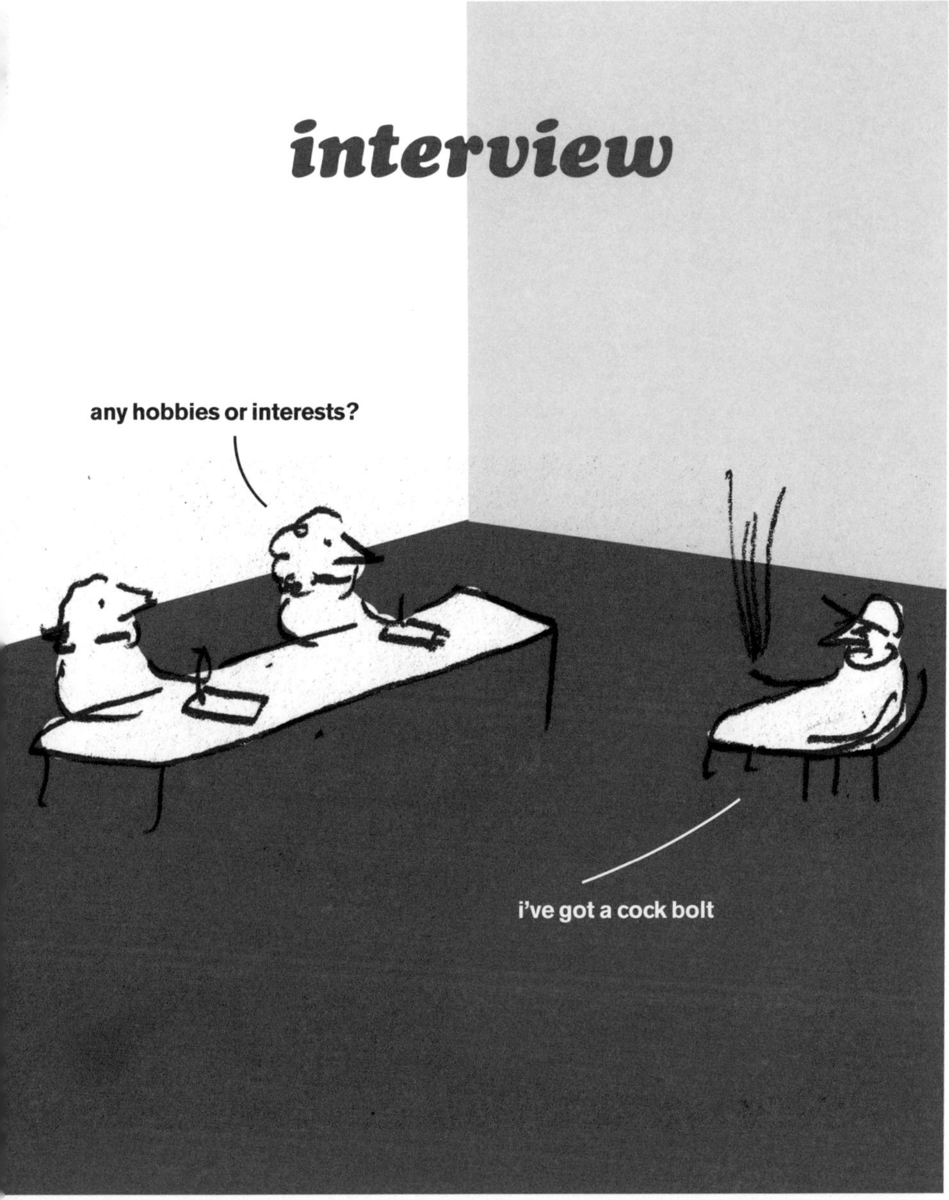

work

work

I'm thinking about leaving,
do you want to have a whip round for my present and I'll see if it's worth it

work

so if i keep not coming in, you're going to start not paying me?

work

worth a punt

my wife's just had another baby, it's not mine but can I have a couple of weeks off anyway

Sir Paul Pot
CEO & Chairman

work

you can't bring a dog into work
er hello? he's not actually working

leaving present

we couldn't think what to get you for a present, so we had a whip round and put 40 quid in the snack machine
jammed it right up, anyway the maintenance department are on their way up and they owe you 40 mars bars

work

you want a pay rise because you've given up smoking?
yeah I used to do about 2 hours a day on fag breaks, now i've given up I'm not spending that time working unless you pay me more money

contract enquiry

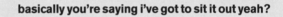

Sir Paul Pot

CEO & Chairman

seasonal opportunity

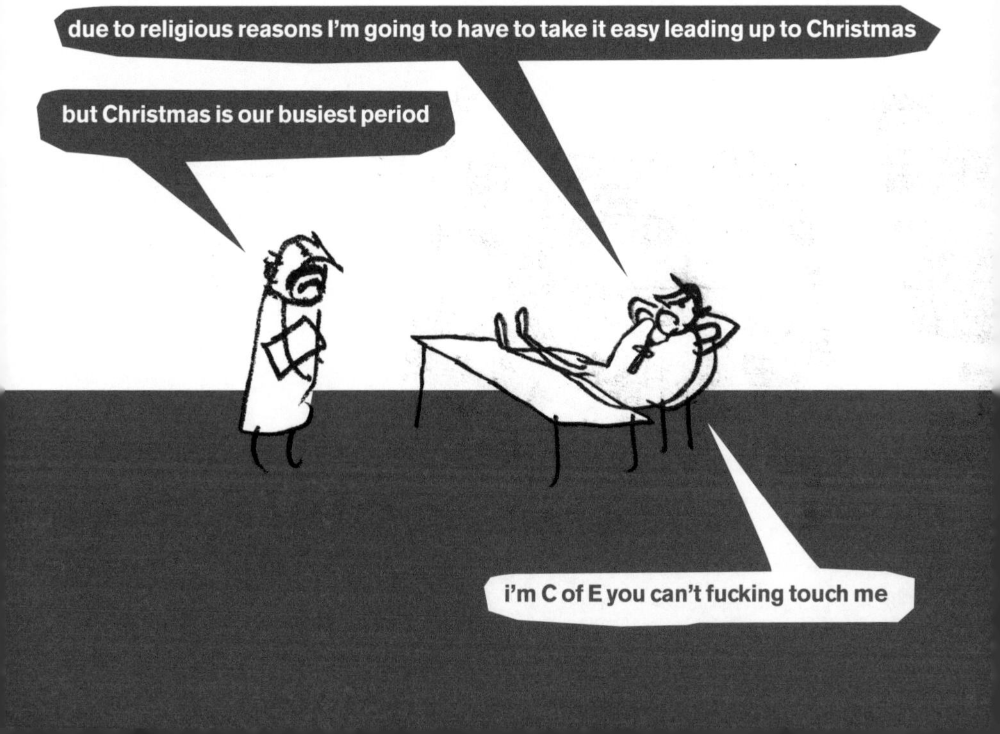

appraisal

we would like to point out to you that it's highly unprofessional to refer to us as 'the cunts upstairs' when sending emails to our client database

I think I'll go home, I'm a bit bored

team building

Sir Paul Pot

CEO & Chairman

work

I got this work finished quicker than normal, what way is it to the bonus department?

all i want you to do is admit your company made a mistake

there's a fucking good chance we did, but i can't do that in case they're recording it

work

work

executive burnout

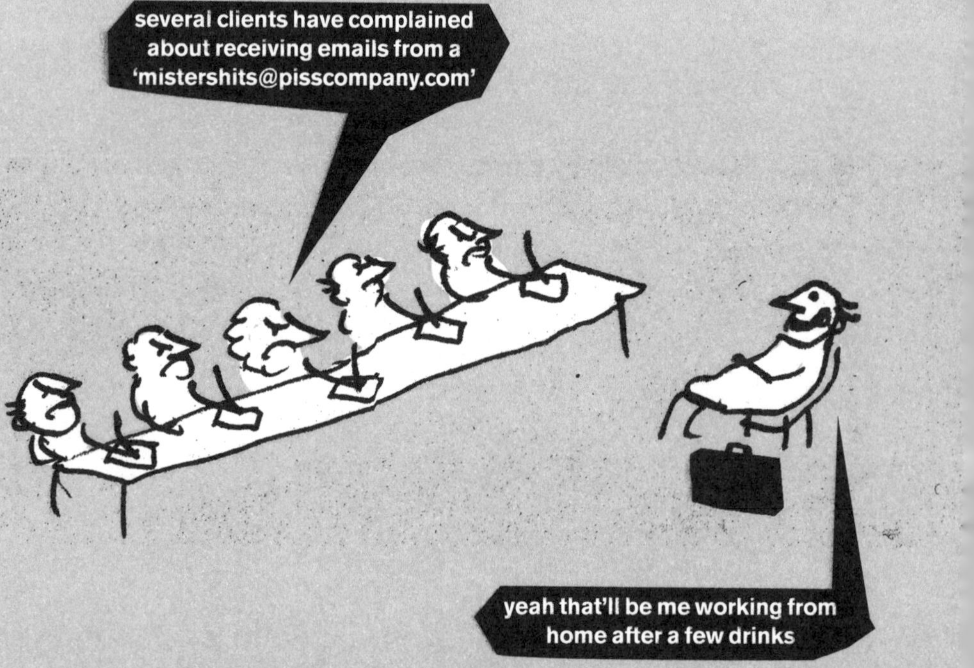

work

you want to book two weeks sick leave in August?

yeah I'm off to Spain to get my tits done

flexi-time

acccording to our records you've only worked afternoons for the past six months
yeah I get pissed up in the morning. Then I come in here and have a lie down in the cupboard

Sir Paul Pot
CEO & Chairman

interview sideline
sorry you haven't got the job, here's the bill for your tea and biscuits

water cooler moment

interview